THE MAHABHARATA

CHILDREN'S ILLUSTRATED CLASSICS

THE GAME of DICE

Retold by **CHARU AGARWAL DHANDIA**
Art **KAVITA SINGH KALE** *Design* **RACHITA RAKYAN**

Published by
Rupa Publications India Pvt. Ltd 2020
7/16, Ansari Road, Daryaganj
New Delhi 110002

Sales centres:
Allahabad Bengaluru Chennai
Hyderabad Jaipur Kathmandu
Kolkata Mumbai

Edition copyright © Rupa Publications Pvt. Ltd 2020

All rights reserved.
No part of this publication may be reproduced, transmitted,
or stored in a retrieval system, in any form or by any means, electronic, mechanical, photocopying,
recording or otherwise,
without the prior permission of the publisher.

ISBN: 978-81-291-4975-6

First impression 2020

10 9 8 7 6 5 4 3 2 1

The moral right of the author has been asserted.

Printed at Nutech Print Services - India

This book is sold subject to the condition that it shall not, by way of trade or otherwise, be lent, resold, hired out, or otherwise circulated, without the publisher's prior consent, in any form of binding or cover other than that in which it is published.

Charu Agarwal Dhandia weaves together her two biggest passions—studying Indian classical literature and creative storytelling. She is an economist by training and works in the social development space.

Kavita Singh Kale's background as an artist and a designer enables her to draw a thin line between design following functionality and pure self-expression. This has helped her evolve as a transmedia artist. Her work includes art installations, children's books, comics, paintings and videos.

Rachita Rakyan combines over 15 years of expertise in graphic design and art direction with deep understanding of functionality and aesthetics across print, publishing, branding and digital media.

CONTENTS

KURU DYNASTY — IV-V
KEY CHARACTERS — VI-VII
THE CITY OF INDRAPRASTHA — 1
THE YAGNA CEREMONY — 7
DURYODHANA'S FURY — 13
SHAKUNI'S PLAN — 25
INVITATION TO THE PANDAVAS — 35

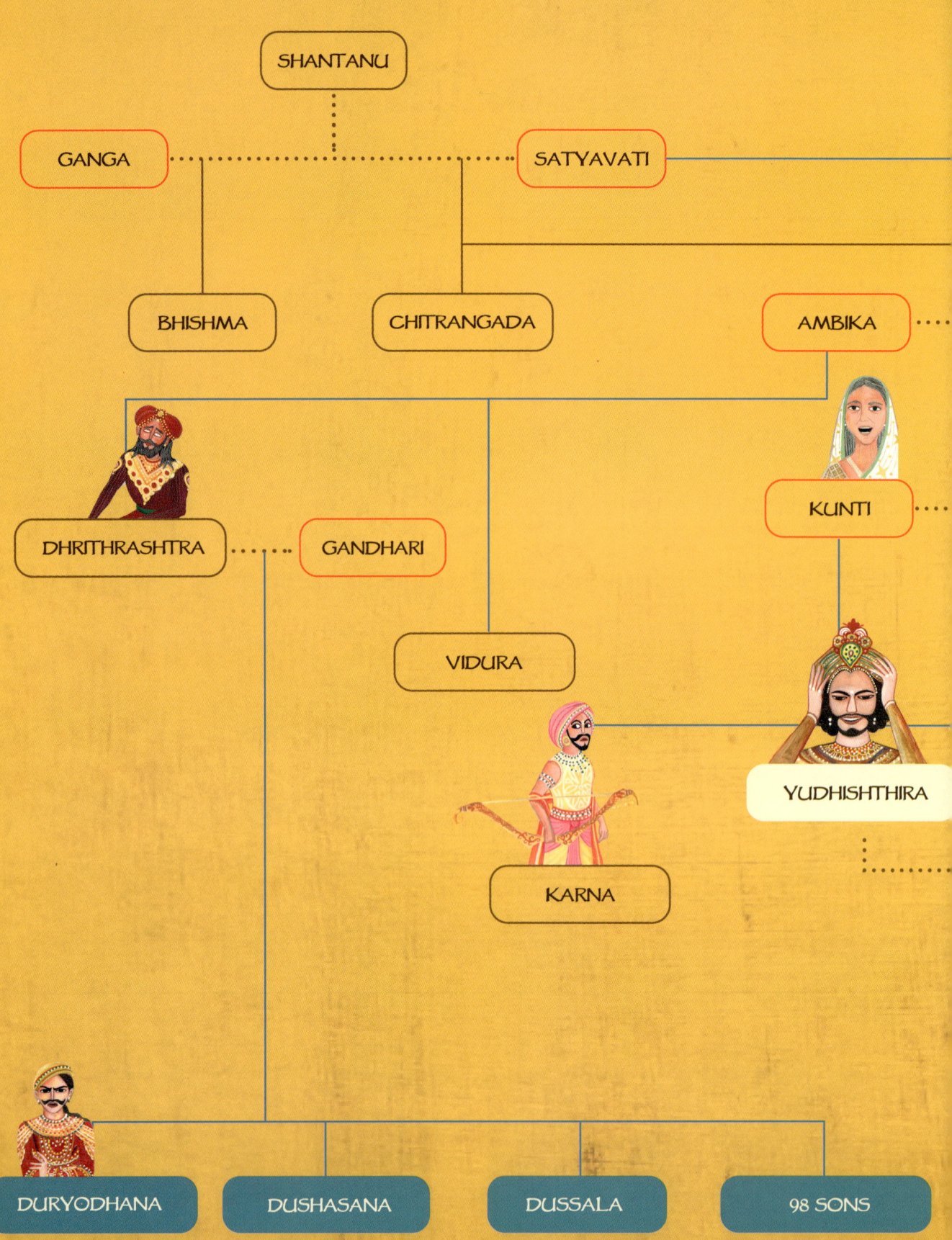

KURU DYNASTY

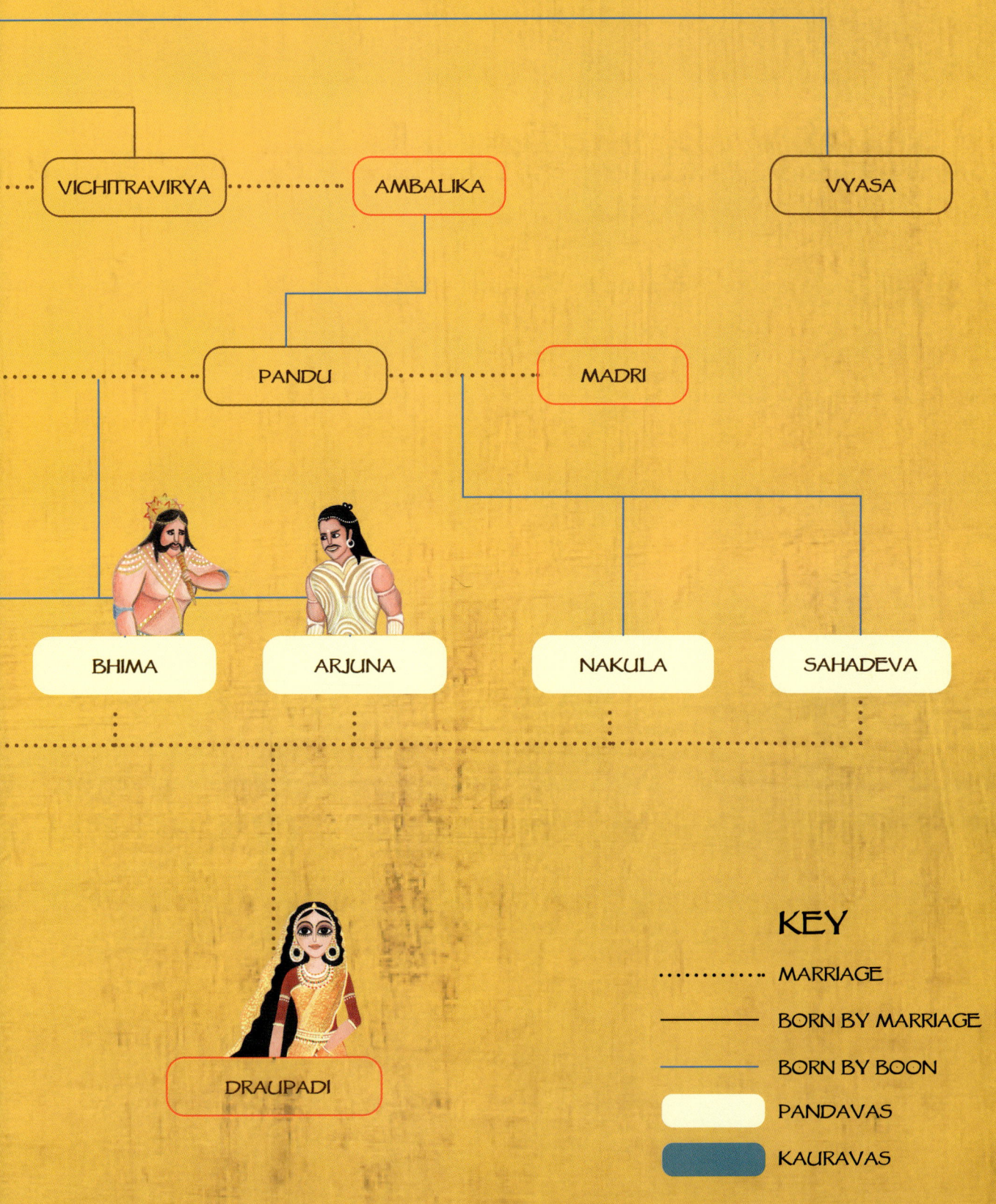

KEY

.... MARRIAGE

⸻ BORN BY MARRIAGE

⸻ BORN BY BOON

▢ PANDAVAS

▮ KAURAVAS

KEY CHARACTERS

DURYODHANA

Duryodhana was the eldest brother amongst the Kauravas and born to princess Gandhari as a blessing from sage Vyasa. He was very jealous of the Pandavas.

YUDHISHTHIRA

Yudhishthira was the eldest Pandava born to Kunti as a blessing from Lord Dharma. He ruled Indraprashtha and later Hastinapur. Yudhishthira proved to be a great ruler and was known for his virtues of honesty, loyalty, justice, tolerance and brotherhood.

SHAKUNI

Shakuni was the maternal uncle of the Kauravas. He was very close to Duryodhana and an accomplice in his plans and tricks against the Pandavas. He had a magical marble dice which he used to trick the Pandavas in the historic game of dice in Hastinapur.

KRISHNA

Krishna was the prince of Dwarka and cousin brother of the Pandavas and Kauravas. He was a great friend and advisor to Arjuna and loved the Pandavas dearly. He played a critical role in the creation of Indraprastha and later in the Kurukshetra War.

DHRITHRASHTRA

Dhrithrashtra was the blind king of Hastinapur. He was born to Queen Ambika by a boon given to her by the great sage Vyasa. Dhrithrashtra married Gandhari, daughter of the King of Gandhar. Together, they had hundred sons called the Kauravas and a daughter called Dussala.

DRAUPADI

Draupadi was a young and beautiful girl, born from the flames of a fire yagna to King Drupada of Panchala, along with her brother Dhrishtadyumna. When Drapaudi grew up, Arjuna won her swayamvar and eventually she married all the five Pandavas.

THE CITY OF INDRAPRASTHA

Duryodhana was the eldest of the Kauravas. He wanted to become the King of Hastinapur. But the Pandavas were stronger, wiser and more skilled than him. So, Duryodhana and his father Dhrithrashtra tricked the Pandavas and gifted them a piece of land near Hastinapur. This land was useless and of no good to them.

The Pandavas graciously accepted the gift but did not know what to do with it. On the advice of the mighty Krishna, they built a beautiful city called Indraprastha there.

Soon Indraprastha became a land of peace and prosperity. Yudhishthira, the eldest of the Pandavas, was the King of Indraprastha.

Yudhishthira worked day and night to make his people happy and wealthy. The people loved him for his kindness.

They named him Ajatashatru, a person with no enemies. The fame of the Pandavas soon started spreading far and wide.

THE YAGNA CEREMONY

One day, Yudhishthira announced that he would perform the powerful Rajasuya *yagna* for the good of the kingdom. Preparations began on a grand scale with great excitement. Kings from all over the country were invited. Huge mansions and palaces were built for them to stay.

Yudhishthira sent his brothers to invite the kings. Nakula and Sahadeva reached Hastinapur to invite Bhishma, Dhrithrashtra, Dronacharya and Duryodhana to the ceremony.

They accepted the invitation and agreed to become a part of the ceremony in Indraprastha.

The day of the *yagna* arrived. All the kings and sages took their seats around the holy *yagna* fire. With the blessings of the Gods, the ceremony took place. The next day, the kings began leaving for their kingdoms.

DURYODHANA'S FURY

Duryodhana had heard a lot of praise about Indraprastha. He decided to stay back for a few more days to look around the city.

The Pandavas were good hosts. They took great care of Duryodhana. Every morning, Duryodhana would leave the palace and roam around the city. He saw huge buildings with polished floors and carved pillars.

He saw how happy the people were. He noticed how they cheered their king, Yudhishthira, wherever he went. All this made Duryodhana angry and jealous. He realized that his kingdom, Hastinapur, had not become as rich and prosperous as Indraprastha. His subjects were not as happy too.

He was also angry that his subjects did not love or respect him as the people of Indraprastha respected Yudhishthira.

One day while walking down a corridor in the palace, Duryodhana noticed some water on the floor. He picked up his robe so that it would not get wet.

Nakula, who was passing by, saw Duryodhana do this. He said, 'Brother Duryodhana, there is no water on the floor! It is only the polished floor, shining like a mirror!'

Duryodhana was embarrassed. He felt like a fool and hurried back to his chambers.

The next morning, as Duryodhana was walking by, he suddenly banged into something that he could not see. Duryodhana held his forehead and wondered what had happened.
Bhima heard the loud thud and rushed to Duryodhana.

He saw Duryodhana and understood what had happened. Bhima said, 'Brother, you hurt yourself because you walked into a glass door. You could not see it. It is so clean that it seems invisible!'

Duryodhana again felt embarrassed and left without saying anything. He felt that the Pandavas had planned to fool him.

In the evening, while walking, Duryodhana saw a pool of water. He remembered what had happened to him in front of Nakula. He did not want to be fooled again. So he went ahead thinking there was nothing. As soon as he took a step, he slipped and fell right into the water!

He got up completely drenched. Draupadi and her friends saw Duryodhana get up and burst into laughter. Duryodhana heard them laugh and got furious. He decided to leave Indraprastha immediately.

SHAKUNI'S PLAN

Duryodhana returned to Hastinapur. One day, he said to his brother Dushasana and uncle Shakuni, 'I have been miserable from the time I have returned from Indraprastha. They fooled me and I want to take revenge.' Shakuni knew that the Pandavas were very clever and it would be difficult to trick them.

One evening, Shakuni was sitting in his chambers when an idea struck him. He quickly walked to Duryodhana's chambers. He said, 'I have a plan to defeat the Pandavas. We know Yudhishthira loves to gamble. We must invite the Pandavas for a game of dice in Hastinapur.'

Duryodhana jumped up in excitement.

'That's a great idea, uncle! I want to defeat Yudhishthira in my own palace. But there is a problem. I do not know how to play the game of dice.'

'I will play on your behalf,' replied Shakuni. He pulled out a beautiful marble dice from his pocket. 'This is a magical dice. This will help us defeat Yudhishthira. But we will need Dhrithrashtra's permission to invite the Pandavas,' said Shakuni.

The next day, Shakuni went to Dhrithrashtra and told him about their plan to invite the Pandavas to Hastinapur. Dhrithrashtra was unsure of the plan but he agreed as he wanted to see Duryodhana happy.

Construction of a huge hall began for the game to be played. The hall was called Jayanta. Thousands of masons and carvers were invited to build the magnificent hall.

INVITATION TO THE PANDAVAS

Vidura was the minister of the court and very fond of the Pandavas. He had saved them from Duryodhana's evil plans in the past. When he came to know about Jayanta being specially constructed for the planned game of dice with the Pandavas, he got worried. He knew something must be wrong. So he went to Indraprastha to inform the Pandavas about the game.

When Yudhishthira received Duryodhana's invitation, he got excited about the game and gladly accepted it. The other Pandava brothers disliked Yudhishthira's love for gambling. They were wary of Duryodhana's intentions and did not want to go to Hastinapur.
But Yudhishthira did not listen to their advice.

The Pandavas reached Hastinapur. They were received by the people amid great celebrations. The entire kingdom was waiting to witness the game of dice between the Pandavas and the Kauravas.

It was the day of the game. The Kauravas, Pandavas and ministers of the court got seated for the game to begin. Duryodhana announced, 'Welcome to this great game! As you know, I do not know how to gamble. So uncle Shakuni will play on my behalf.'

There were murmurs in the crowd. The Pandavas knew that Shakuni would trick them in the game and win. Duryodhana said, 'LET'S BEGIN!'

Yudhishthira and Shakuni sat opposite each other and the game began. Both of them gambled with money, jewels and other precious things. Shakuni used his magical dice and kept winning. Yudhishthira lost one round after the other and soon lost everything. He even lost his kingdom to Shakuni.

All the Pandava brothers, Vidura and Bhishma, tried to stop Yudhishthira from playing any more. They were afraid of what would happen if Yudhishthira continued losing.
But Yudhishthira wanted to play on so that he could get back everything that he had lost.

Soon Yudhishthira had nothing left to bet. Then without thinking he betted his brothers, himself and their wife Draupadi.
And he lost everything!

Everyone in the hall was shocked! They could not believe what was happening. No one had ever seen a game of dice like this.

Yudhishthira finally had nothing left to bet. He turned to Duryodhana and said, 'I have lost all that I had. All of us are your slaves now.'

Duryodhana's happiness knew no bounds. He had finally won over the Pandavas. Nobody could challenge him now.

Draupadi had been standing in a corner and watching all this happen. She felt miserable.

Dhrithrashtra whispered to Draupadi, 'I return Indraprastha to you. You and the Pandavas should leave Hastinapur at once!'

Duryodhana heard this and said, 'No father, the last round of dice is still to be played. Whoever loses this, will spend the next thirteen years in the forest.'
Yudhishthira agreed to play and lost this round too. The Pandavas and Draupadi left for the Kamyaka forest to spend the next thirteen years in exile.

TITLES IN THIS SERIES

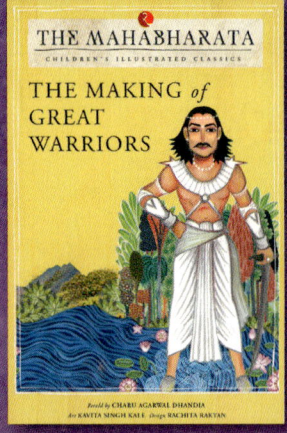
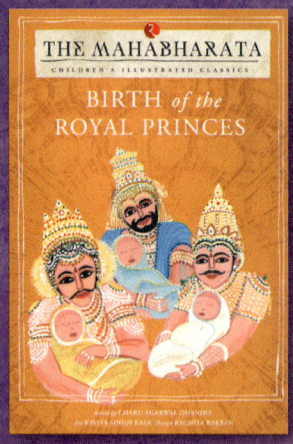
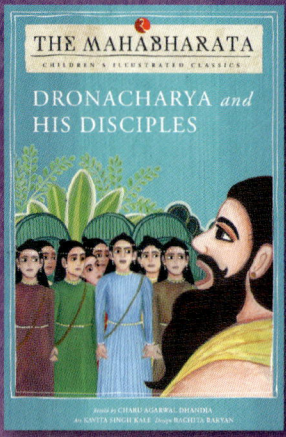
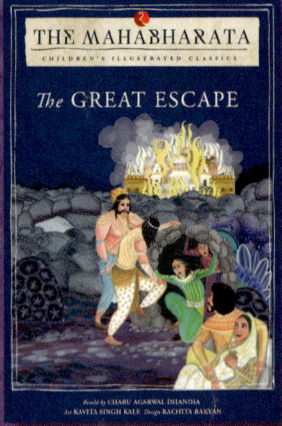
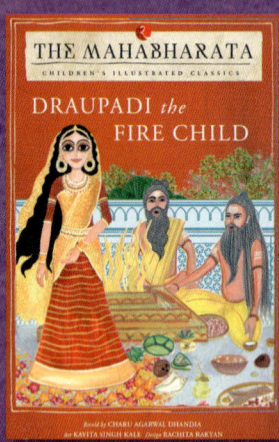
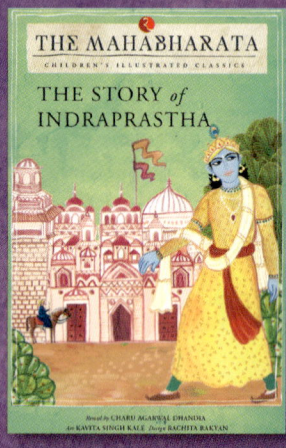
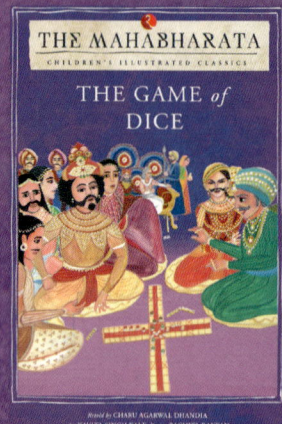
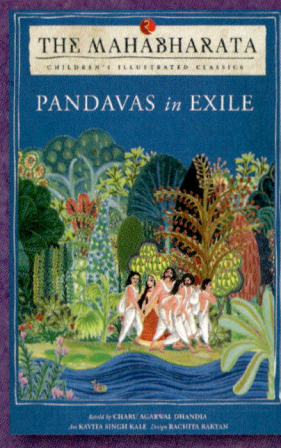
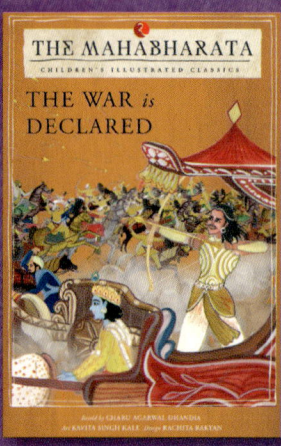